THIS IS ME
AND
ADHD

WRITTEN BY
SHERRIE SPERLING, LCSW

ILLUSTRATED BY
TIFFANY GORDON

For more information visit
ReadLearnandShare.com

To my nieces,
Hayden and Holly

For your fun energy, laughter,
courage, inner beauty,
innocence and creativity.

May God bless you each day!

I love you both!

Hi, my name is Tommy!

Often my thoughts wander
here, there, and everywhere.

My thoughts are like a speeding train.
I try to focus on one thing and my thoughts
come rushing to my brain.
Here, there, and everywhere.

At school, my teacher greets me with a smile.

She asks, "Where is your homework?"

"I have not seen it for a while."

6

I stumble as I look through my backpack for the papers
my teacher needs.

There are papers here, there, and everywhere.

I completed some assignments days before the due date.

My teacher asks, "Why are you turning in your work so late?"

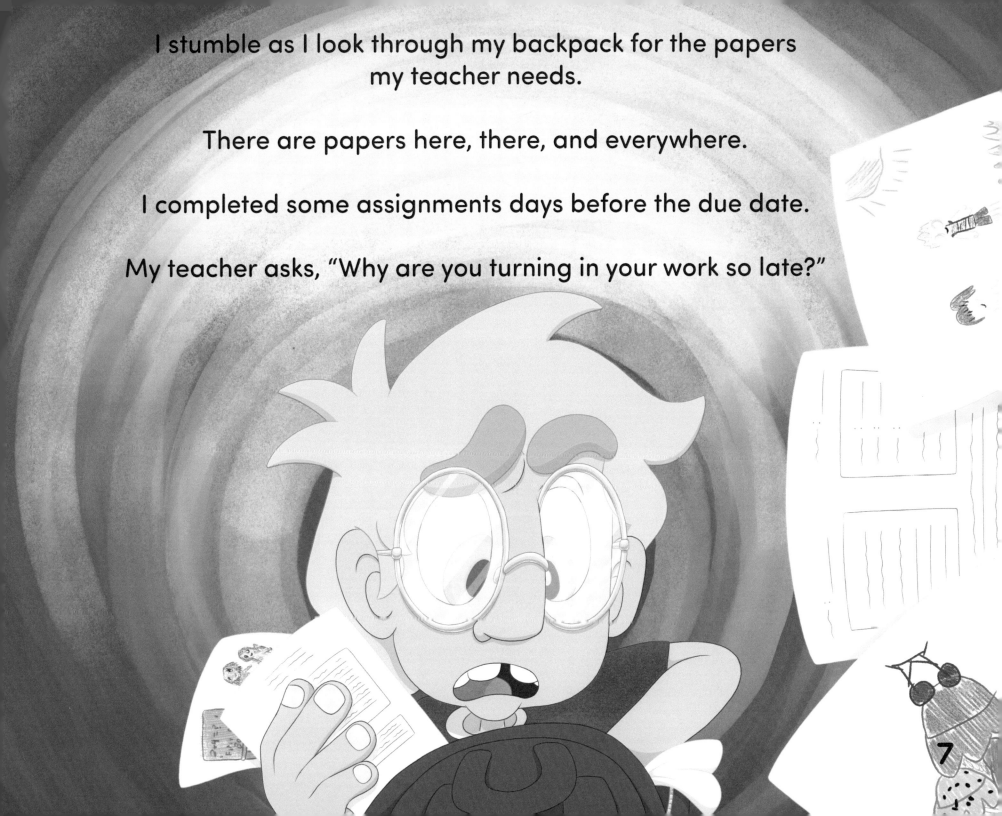

Before I can answer, the bell rings,
signaling the class to play outside.

The teacher tells everyone to line up side by side.

Sometimes, I have so much energy,
and it's challenging to stand in one place.

I run here, there, and everywhere
as if I'm in a race.

My teacher tells me
to tighten my fists or march
at a slow and steady pace.

9

The school day ends,
and I can't wait to get home
and take a rest.

My mom says,
"No, no, no, you have
to study for a math test."

10

My brain feels so tired after
a long day at school.

I stomp up the stairs yelling,
"I want to play a game or two!"

My mom allows a 30-minute rest before
I need to sit down and study for the test.

11

Bedtime comes, and my thoughts are here, there, and everywhere.

I am unable to go to sleep.

My dad says, "Let's try
the roller coaster breath technique*."

12

"Trace each finger up with an inhale and exhale while tracing down."

I repeat the technique five times and realize my brain is calming down.

Now I am relaxed.

INHALE

INHALE

INHALE

INHALE

INHALE

INHALE

EXHALE

EXHALE

EXHALE

EXHALE

*

I talk to Abby.
I talk to Jimmy.

I talk to Billy,
and I talk to Timmy.

15

I see a squirrel, a tree,
and a fluffy dog with brown hair.
Once again, I recognize
my thoughts are everywhere.

17

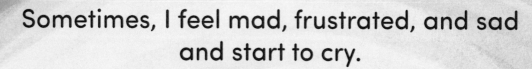

Sometimes, I feel mad, frustrated, and sad and start to cry.

18

When my teacher asks the reason,
I really do not know why.

My school day ends,
and my mom greets me
at the door, saying

"Your bedroom is such a mess."

"There are clothes,
dolls, and crayons
all over the floor."

Cleaning my bedroom is
not my favorite chore.

20

I look under the bed, and to my surprise,
I find a lost library book,
old school assignment,
some candy,
and four dimes.

21

Bedtime comes, and
my thoughts are
here, there,
and everywhere.
My eyes close tight
with all my might
in hopes of falling asleep.
I even try my dad's suggestion
of slowly counting sheep.
One sheep, two sheep,
three sheep four...

...Now my focus is on the crayons
along the floor.

22

I close my eyes and think of butterflies, rainbows and sheep.
Soon thereafter, I fall asleep.

23

My parents sit down to talk with me
regarding my attention span.

We all agree to meet with Dr. Stan.

After meeting with the doctor for
tests, questions, and history,

Dr. Stan tells me I have ADHD.

Wow, that explains the fast energy, wandering mind and thoughts of many.

That explains the messy backpack, bedroom and desk at school.

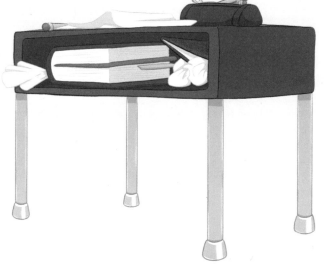

That explains at school and home not always following every rule.

CLOCK

AGENDA

LISTS

After meeting with Dr. Stan,
my mom and dad helped me organize my day
using an alarm, an agenda
and to do lists along the way.

To help with the bedtime routine of brushing teeth,
taking a bath, and climbing into bed, my parents
create a visual chart for focus in my head.

The chart stays in the bathroom
for me to always see.

So, then I am reminded of
my bedtime routine.

Using my tools helps
me to focus and finish
tasks at home and school.

① BRUSH

② BATH

My doctor reminds me plenty of children and adults with ADHD are intelligent, have colorful thoughts and creativity.

Acknowledgements

I thoroughly enjoyed the journey of writing this book. The people God placed in my life before and during the journey were amazing contributors.
Thank you, God, for your guidance and blessings.

I am so grateful to my husband, Mark.
Thank you for your support, encouragement, words of wisdom and love.

 Thank you mom for your love and suppport.

I am grateful to the illustrator, Tiffany Gordon.
Thank you for keeping me on track with accountability and deadlines.
Your patience on this journey was remarkable.
Your talent and knowledge are amazing.

Thank you to Dr. Foluso Solarin, Licensed Psychologist,
for your time, words of wisdom and our writing sessions.

To Kelli O'Neill, LPC, thank you for your support, encouragement and feedback.

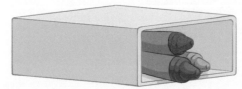

Resources and Suggestions

- Break tasks down for child
(e.g., when cleaning room, place toys on shelf, shoes in the closet)
- Ask child to repeat instructions
- Utilize timers, agendas, to do lists, and visual charts as reminders
- Allow breaks between completing homework assignments
- Talk with school on IEP plan for accommodations in test taking
- Provide consistent reassurance and validation to child's feelings
- Implement daily structure/routine
- End of week check-ins to review positives
- Talk to child's pediatrician or psychologist regarding ADHD evaluation
- Have child participate in a sport for physical outlet
  and to promote team building and socialization skills
- Consistent sleep patterns

Other resources on education, dietary restrictions,
and supplements for ADHD include:
- Children and Adults with
Attention-Deficit/Hyperactivity (CHADD)
- National Institute of Mental Health (NIMH)

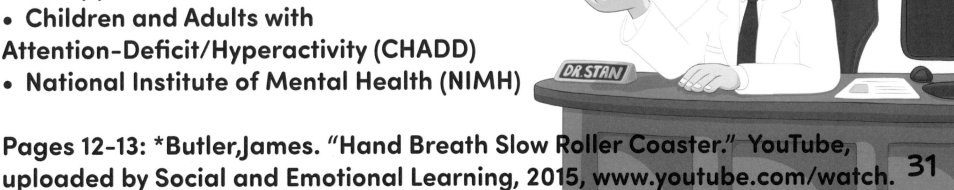

Pages 12-13: *Butler,James. "Hand Breath Slow Roller Coaster." YouTube, uploaded by Social and Emotional Learning, 2015, www.youtube.com/watch.

About The Author

Sherrie Sperling, LCSW, is an upcoming children's author residing in Woodstock, Georgia. As a Licensed Clinical Social Worker, Sherrie has worked with children and families for the past 12 years. She saw the impact of an ADHD diagnosis had on children and their families.

Fueled for years by a desire to normalize and educate children and parents on ADHD, Sherrie joined a writing group and began the process.

As a member of the Society of Children's Book writers and Illustrators (SCBWI), she has gained experience, education and support within the community.

When Sherrie is not writing or working with clients, she enjoys playing with her three fur babies Baxter, dog and two cats, Chloe and Gracie.

Sherrie can be found on psychologytoday.com
and
readlearnandshare.com

Milton Keynes UK
Ingram Content Group UK Ltd.
UKRC030730020624
443433UK00001B/1

9 7989 89 9968718